Action for the Environment

Water Supplies

Jude Welton

W
FRANKLIN WATTS
LONDON · SYDNEY

Franklin Watts
96 Leonard Street
London EC2A 4XD

Franklin Watts Australia
45–51 Huntley Street
Alexandria
NSW 2015

ISBN: 0 7496 5536 4

A CIP catalogue record for this book is
available from the British Library

Printed in Malaysia

Editor: Adrian Cole
Design: Proof Books
Art Director: Jonathan Hair
Picture Researcher: Kathy Lockley

Acknowledgements

AA World Travel Library: 9t. ACDI/CIDA. Photo: Roger
LeMoyne 24b. APL/Art Directors & TRIP Photo Library: 23
b. ApproTec/Photo by Martin Fisher 15. Bojan Brecelj/Still
Pictures: 20, 28t. Robert Brook/Science Photo Library: 12.
Andrew Davies/Still Pictures: 23t. M & C Denis-Huot/
Still Pictures: 24t. © Digital Vision Ltd. All rights 4b.
Pierre Dunnigan/Still Pictures: 28b. Ecover 19b.
Mark Edwards/Still Pictures: 10t. Findhorn Foundation 11b.
Peter Frischmuth/Still Pictures: 7tr. Spencer Grant/
Art Directors & TRIP Photo Library: 9b. Ron Giling/
Still Pictures: Cover tl. Paul Harrison/Still Pictures: 14.
ITDG/ZUL 27. Nick Molnar 19t. Gil Moti/Still Pictures: 29.
Christine Osborne/Ecoscene: Cover b, Title page, 21b. "PA"
Photos 25. Ray Pfortner/Still Pictures: 22, 31. © Copyright
1996 PhotoDisc, Inc. All rights reserved: Cover tr, 18. Rex
Features 2, 8 tr, 8bl, 17, 26b. Helene Rogers/Art Directors &
TRIP Photo Library: 13b. Roy Consultants Group Ltd 11t.
Mike Schroder/Still Pictures: 16. Timothy Soar 10b. Jochen
Tack/Still Pictures: 26t. © Tom Wagner/CORBIS SABA 13t.
WaterAid 21t. WaterAid/Somesh 5, 6–7.

Contents

The blue planet

People need water to survive. For many, clean water comes at the turn of a tap inside their home. But others have to walk long distances, just to fetch water that may be unsafe to drink. We can work together to bring clean, safe water to everyone.

THE WATER CYCLE

The Earth's water goes round in a process called the water cycle. But there is not an endless supply across our planet. In some places water is scarce, and even in well-watered countries people often use water more quickly than it is replaced.

2 **3**

1

1. Heated by the Sun, water from oceans and rivers evaporates (turns into a gas, water vapour), and rises into the sky. 2. In the cooler air, the vapour condenses (changes back to a liquid) to form clouds. 3. These droplets of water fall to Earth as rain and the cycle starts again.

PRECIOUS RESOURCE

Earth is sometimes called the 'blue planet' because almost 75% of it is covered in water. But most of this is salty sea water, and we need fresh water to drink and grow crops. Only 0.1% of the world's water is available for human use.

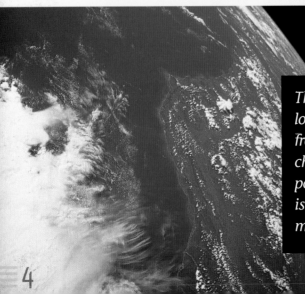

The Earth's water supply looks plentiful when viewed from space. But climate changes and an increasing population mean that there is less water available, and more people who need it.

Action stations

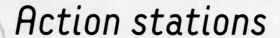

One of the simplest ways to increase water supplies is to 'tap into' the water cycle, by 'harvesting' rain.

The charity WaterAid and its partner REEDS (Research in Environment, Education and Development Society) helped villagers in Hasmabad in India to build three water tanks to collect and store rainwater from the school roof.

Your family can harvest rainwater too, simply by installing a water butt. Your school could become involved in fundraising activities to help WaterAid's work (see website, page 31).

Rainwater collected in the tanks, like the one being constructed here, is filtered with sand and charcoal to make it safe to drink. Simple methods such as this can improve – and even save – people's lives.

Hidden treasure

Most of the Earth's fresh water is stored below ground as groundwater. If too much is used too quickly, or if there is a drought, this vital water source does not have a chance to refill.

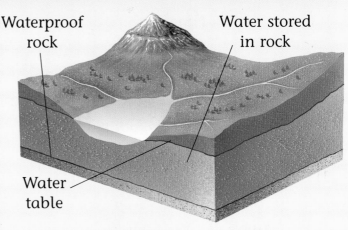

Waterproof rock

Water stored in rock

Water table

TAKING TOO MUCH

Two billion people depend on groundwater for drinking water, and industry and agriculture use increasingly large amounts. In India, between 1960 and 1990, the number of tube wells used to access groundwater for irrigation increased from 3,000 to 6 million.

AQUIFERS

Rainwater soaks into the ground until it reaches a layer of waterproof rock. The water collects above in a layer of porous rock, which holds water like a giant sponge. This water store is called an aquifer.

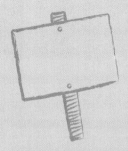

Action stations

Freshwater springs provide many cities, towns and villages across the world with a source of water. For example, most of the drinking water in Florida, USA, comes from a huge aquifer and the freshwater springs that rise from it. Florida's Department of Environmental Protection realised that people would be less likely to damage these hidden, natural treasures by overuse and pollution if they knew about them – so they made a documentary (see www.floridasprings.org).

Since the Roman era, Italians have been keen drinkers of spring water. Many towns and villages have spring water fountains, some of which date back many centuries, for the use of residents and visitors.

Filling up bottles from a spring water fountain in Lucca, Italy. People have been protecting and using freshwater springs like this for centuries.

WHEN THE WELL RUNS DRY

The well in the village of Thada, India, dried up because less rain fell and farmers used too much water. The water table dropped and water could no longer be reached. A simple drainage system solved the problem. Waste water was collected, filtered and channelled into a soak pit. The water table rose, and water could be pumped from the well again.

This hand pump in the Indian village of Thada is used to draw water up from a well, which was once dry because the local water table dropped.

Turning the tap

Almost all water has to be treated to make it safe to drink. In the developed world, water companies collect water from rivers, reservoirs or underground sources, purify it and pipe it into everyone's homes. But for millions of people, there is no clean water supply.

Some countries charge people for water according to how much they use. The amount is measured by meters, such as these ones, installed in their homes. Keeping track of how much water is used can help people to use less.

A burst water pipe in London. In older cities, water companies are now working to replace the underground pipes, which can be over 100 years old.

HOW MUCH DO WE USE?
Perhaps because people in the developed world get clean water at the turn of a tap, they often forget how precious water is, and use it wastefully. A city dweller in the USA uses about 500 litres per day, while an African villager might use about 30 litres.

MENDING LEAKS
In some countries, such as the UK, more than a third of water in the supply network is lost through leaking pipes. Water companies are responsible for most repairs. A dripping tap can waste a litre of water every hour. To save water, check the taps in your home, and ask an adult to repair any ones that drip.

Action stations

Raising public awareness can help protect our water supplies. In Turkey, many people, including politicians and hotel owners, took part in a project by WWF (World Wide Fund for Nature) aimed at saving water. Owners of hotels gave tourists leaflets containing lots of ideas about saving water. The success of the project has inspired other countries to join in.

Tourists in front of a hotel in Icmeler, Turkey. Turkish hotel owners have been involved in a project to save water supplies.

SOME TIPS FOR SAVING WATER IN YOUR HOME

• Never leave a tap running if you are not using the water.

• Turn off the tap when brushing your teeth. Design a poster, and put it up above the sink to remind the whole family.

• Take short showers rather than deep baths, and save up to 30%. (A five-minute shower uses 30 litres of water; a bath takes 90 litres.)

• If you do not have a low-flush or dual-flush toilet, ask an adult to put a brick or a 'hippo' (a special plastic bag full of water) into the cistern. This reduces the amount of water used in each flush.

• Collect water used for washing vegetables and fruit in a bowl, and water your house plants with it.

Down the drain

While some pipes carry clean water into our homes, other pipes transport dirty water out. Before dirty water is allowed back into the water supply, it goes through a long and expensive cleaning process to make it safe to use.

These jars show the different stages of water treatment (left to right), which gradually remove solids from water. But cleaning water is expensive.

TREATING SEWAGE

The used water from toilets, bathrooms and kitchens is called sewage. It travels along pipes to a sewage treatment plant, where solids are removed, and 'friendly' bacteria and other microbes purify the water by removing harmful organisms. Chemicals used in the process can harm the environment.

This modern sewage treatment works is completely covered and designed to blend in with its surroundings.

COSTLY TREATMENT

Treating sewage in a treatment plant is costly, and many developing countries cannot afford to do it. In some parts of the developing world, up to 90% of sewage re-enters the water system without being treated at all – often carrying water-borne diseases that can kill.

REED BEDS

A cheaper, more environmentally-friendly way to clean waste water is to use reed beds. Reeds grow in shallow water, which they filter and purify naturally. The plant roots use nutrients from the sewage to help them grow.

Reed beds have been used increasingly since the 1960s to clean dirty and polluted water.

Action stations

As part of a plan to create an ecovillage, the Findhorn Foundation in Scotland opened Europe's first Living Machine in 1995. The Living Machine uses a series of tanks to treat sewage from the population of around 300 people at the Foundation.

The tanks contain bacteria and other micro-organisms, plants, snails and fish that purify the water. This natural method is chemical-free, and cleans the water to a higher standard than European guidelines. There are about 20 Living Machines in use, including two used by the Body Shop for cleaning human and industrial waste.

The Living Machine, like this one in Scotland, is based on the same natural principles as reed-bed technology, but works more quickly, uses much less space and can be housed in a large greenhouse.

Water, work and leisure

Water is needed for almost everything we make and use. Huge amounts are used by industry, while even leisure facilities, such as golf courses, swallow up precious water. However, there are ways to use and waste less.

Water is a vital part of industry. This sea water is used by a gas-fired power station. It condenses the steam that drives the station's turbines.

INDUSTRIAL SAVINGS

Industry uses 20% of the water we consume – for everything from producing cars to making this book. But this amount is being reduced as companies become more water-efficient. For example, industrial water use dropped by one fifth in the USA between 1980 and 2003. In Japan, industrial water use has been reduced by a quarter since 1970.

Action stations

Some industrial companies are reducing the damage that their factories can do to the environment. As part of its environmental policy, Kobe Steel in Japan has developed new technologies and processes that reduce water wastage and water pollution.

Waste water is not pumped out into the public water supply. Instead, it is treated in the factory so that it can be used again in the industrial process. Almost 100% of the Kobe Steel water is recycled in this way.

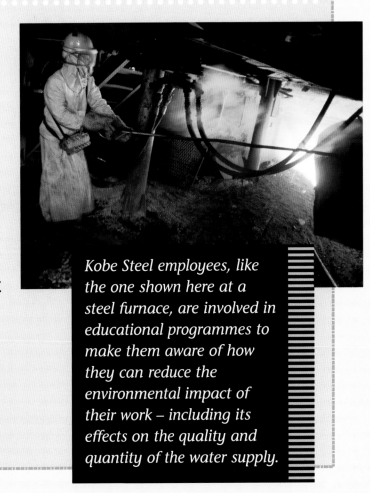

Kobe Steel employees, like the one shown here at a steel furnace, are involved in educational programmes to make them aware of how they can reduce the environmental impact of their work – including its effects on the quality and quantity of the water supply.

GREEN GREENS

In some parts of the world, water sprinklers pour out water on to grassy areas, such as golf courses, to keep them looking attractive. This is especially wasteful if the water used has gone through the long and costly process to make it of drinking quality.

Water used to irrigate public parks and golf courses does not need to be of drinking quality. For example, some golf courses, including a world-class one in Hawaii, are irrigated with recycled waste water which has been treated but not to drinking quality.

Food and water

Most of the world's fresh water is used to irrigate crops and for farm animals. As the global population increases, there are more people who need food – yet less water is available to grow it. Old ideas and new technologies can help to make the most of the available water.

TRADITIONAL METHODS

For thousands of years, farmers have used simple techniques to make the most of the water that is available. Some build small walls of mud or stone across fields to trap rainwater and allow it to soak into the soil.

A farmer in Mali, West Africa, watering a field that has been laid out with bunds – mud walls that conserve water and prevent soil erosion. Techniques such as this can help to increase crop yields by more than 50%.

Action stations

Many farmers in Kenya have small plots of less than one hectare. They are usually too poor to afford to buy motor-driven water pumps, which have been developed for irrigating larger farms. Until recently, there was no technology available to help them water their crops.

With the aim of matching low-cost, low-tech inventions to the needs of small farmers, a company called Approtec supplies cheap, simple and reliable pedal-driven pumps. Farmers use these to suck up enough groundwater to irrigate their small plots of land.

More than 25,000 Kenyan farmers have benefited from these simple water pumps, which they use to get water to their crops – leading to increased yields and earnings.

DRIP BY DRIP
Growing crops requires a lot of water. Commonly used high-powered water sprinklers are wasteful, because much of the water trickles away or quickly evaporates. Drip irrigation – a system of pipes with holes that deliver water directly to the plants' roots – is being introduced to stop this costly wastage.

Changing climate

Many experts believe that the Earth is heating up. This global warming is changing the world's climate, bringing both droughts and floods. Everyone, from individuals to governments, can help to slow the process down.

GREENHOUSE GASES

The Earth's climate is being changed by global warming. This is caused by greenhouse gases, which are mainly produced by car emissions and the burning of fossil fuels (coal, oil and gas) to make electricity. If global warming continues, flooding will get worse in some places, as the ice at the North and South Poles melts. Other places will become drier – and turn into desert. To avoid this, people are exploring alternative ways to fuel cars and create electricity.

WATER POWER

Hydroelectric power stations use water power to make 'clean' electricity, but they can create environmental and social problems (see page 26). The steam from natural hot water sources, such as hot springs and geysers, can be used to heat homes and water directly, or converted into electricity in a geothermal power station. In some seas and on some shorelines, the energy from waves is also being used to create electricity.

A geothermal power station in New Zealand. It uses hot water and steam from the Earth's core to make electricity.

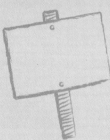

Action stations

In Kyoto, Japan in 1997, some governments agreed to reduce greenhouse gases, in order to stop the floods and droughts caused by global warming.

Campaign groups put pressure on governments to keep their promises. At the World Climate Talks in the Hague in 2002, Friends of the Earth co-ordinated 6,000 people who built a huge water barrier with 50,000 sandbags. This symbolised the threat of flooding posed by global warming. The Dutch environmental minister took several sandbags into the meeting to remind speakers to live up to expectations of the outside world.

In Prague in the Czech Republic, flooding destroyed homes, farmland, roads and people in 2002. Floods occur when water tables rise to the surface and rivers burst their banks. Action by environmental campaign groups draws attention to the dangers of flooding caused by global warming.

Cleaning up our act

Water pollution – for example, the release of untreated sewage and harmful chemicals into rivers or the sea, is a constant threat to the world's water supply. However, new laws, better education and changing attitudes can all make a difference.

ANTI-POLLUTION LAWS

Millions of different chemicals are used in industry and agriculture, many of which can have disastrous effects when they pollute the water supply. In many countries there are now laws preventing industries from polluting rivers or seas. And clean-up projects have successfully made even heavily polluted water clean again.

This is the shocking result of river pollution. The River Rhine in Germany was one of the most polluted rivers in Europe. Now, after an expensive clean-up programme, it is cleaner than it has been in 130 years, and fish and other wildlife have returned to the water.

ORGANIC FARMING

Modern methods of farming grow crops using chemicals. These are often poisonous and can seep into the soil and drain into streams and rivers. Increasing numbers of farmers are growing food using organic methods – without the use of polluting chemicals.

These horses are helping to harvest a field of organically grown potatoes. Instead of using chemicals, organic farmers use natural methods to keep the soil fertile and pest free.

Action stations

We can play our part in reducing water pollution by changing the cleaning products we use. Washing detergents and bleach contaminate the water supply. Using plant-based, environmentally-friendly washing and cleaning products can make a big difference. Ask the adults in your family to buy them if they do not do so already. One of the most well-known manufacturers of these products is the Belgian company Ecover.

These are just some of the environmentally-friendly cleaning products made by Ecover. Their contribution to a cleaner, safer water supply was recognised in 1993, when they were placed on the United Nations Environmental Programme's 'Global 500 Roll of Honour'.

WASHING POWDER
ECOVER
30° 40° 60° 95°

WASHING-UP LIQUID
ECOVER

TOILET CLEANER
ECOVER

ECOVER

ECOVER
DELICATE

Water for all?

We all need water to live, but dirty water can kill. Governments and international agencies, such as the United Nations, have made access to clean, safe water and good sanitation some of their biggest goals.

This pipeline in Egypt is being constructed to carry clean water to towns and villages surrounded by desert.

WHO OWNS WATER?

The companies involved in large-scale water projects are often interested in making profits, and poor people may not be able to afford to pay for water even when it does become available. Campaigners aim to get water to all, not just to those who can afford it.

WORLD WATER FACTS

More than 1 billion people (about 16% of all the people in the world) do not have access to safe drinking water. About 2.4 billion do not have adequate sanitation. Because of this about 3 million people die each year from diseases such as cholera and typhoid, which are spread by water contaminated with human waste. The World Water Forum has set a target of providing water and sanitation for all by the year 2025.

Action stations

Good sanitation and a safe water supply reduce the spread of disease. But educating people about simple health practices, such as using water to wash hands after going to the toilet, are also important.

Promoting safe sanitation saves lives, and it can have unexpected bonuses. In Mozambique, WaterAid has been using 'ecosan' latrines, in which soil and ash are mixed with human waste to decompose into a compost that can be dug out and used for farming.

Using the ecosan latrines in Mozambique helped local people, like this maize farmer, to avoid catching water-borne diseases as well as growing better crops.

WATER ACCESS

In some countries there is plenty of water underground and in rivers, yet clean water remains unavailable to most people. Organisations such as WaterAid help local people to access the natural supply of clean underground water through wells and pumps.

Children on the island of Mafia, off the coast of Tanzania, Africa, raising clean water from a well. Wells are a vital source of water for many people.

21

Clean seas

Salt water needs protecting just as much as fresh water. For years the oceans were used to dump waste, which polluted the water and destroyed marine life. Now, international laws and campaign groups are helping to make our seas – and our beaches – cleaner.

There are schemes, like this one in the USA, that encourage people to keep beaches clean. If you live near a beach, find out if there is a local group that helps to keep it clean and safe.

DON'T LITTER

Whatever we throw away, spill, burn or bury will mix with the world's water. Much of this eventually finds its way, via rivers, to the sea. Never throw litter into rivers or seas. One way to help is to join a beach-cleaning scheme – but make sure there is adult supervision.

CAMPAIGN FOR CLEANER SEAS

Many international agreements have reduced the amount of waste – from raw sewage to industrial chemicals and nuclear waste – being dumped at sea. But a lot of dumping still goes on. Environmental groups, including Greenpeace, keep up the international pressure for cleaner seas.

FLY THE BLUE FLAG

Keeping beaches clean affects the health of humans and the plants and animals that live in or by the sea. One scheme encouraging cleaner beaches is the Blue Flag scheme. In 2003, 2,161 European beaches were judged to be clean enough to display a blue flag.

The Blue Flag scheme began in France in 1985. Since 2001, the scheme has been adopted by many different countries across the world.

Action stations

Even today, untreated sewage is sometimes pumped into the sea, posing a huge health threat to anyone using the water and beaches. Among the most successful protesters against water pollution are Surfers Against Sewage. This pressure group has successfully campaigned for changes to sewage treatment regulations at local, national and international levels.

Surfers realise how important clean seas are – for their own health as well as that of the rest of the planet. They campaign successfully to keep coastlines free from sewage and other forms of water pollution.

Forests and wetlands

Changes made to the natural world have a massive impact on our water supply. As more forests are cut down, and wetlands (such as swamps, bogs and marshes) are drained, the planet's natural systems for storing and purifying water are damaged.

SAVING WETLANDS

Wetlands are essential to maintain the Earth's water supply. They improve water quality, help recharge water supplies, reduce flood risks and support a vast range of wildlife. Half of the world's wetlands were drained for farming or building in the 20th century, but there is now an international movement to protect and reclaim them.

World Wetland Day publicises the importance of wetlands, such as this area in Florida, USA. The day is celebrated on 2 February each year to mark the signing of the Convention on Wetlands in 1971.

WATER STORES

Forest destruction disrupts the water cycle. Forests store rainwater and release it back into the water system gradually. Tree roots also hold soil together, stopping it from being washed away by rainwater.

Following a hurricane that destroyed much of Jamaica's natural forests, government officials established a re-planting programme to prevent the island's soil being washed away.

Action stations

Australia contains many types of wetlands, from lagoons and mangrove forests to billabongs and creeks, but more than half of these have been destroyed. In 1994, Friends of the Earth started a campaign to restore the natural water cycles of inner-city creeks and rivers. One of the most successful actions was at Whites Creek in a suburb of Sydney. What had become an abandoned, weed-infested piece of land was restored to its former role — a freshwater wetland that helps to reduce water pollution, decreases the threat of flooding and supports a wide range of wildlife. Similar sites have been developed in other cities around the world.

This building and observation gallery looks out over 40 hectares of man-made wetland habitat in a built-up area. Such sites can help to protect wildlife as well as providing pleasure for visitors.

FORESTS AND CITIES

Forests not only help to store water, but also act as natural water filters, helping to maintain good-quality water. Authorities in some of the world's major cities now recognise how important nearby forests are to the water supply, and are protecting them with new laws.

Water and electricity

Water can be used to produce electricity. Most hydroelectric schemes use dams to block the flow of rivers and direct water into turbines, which generate electricity. Using water in this way has many benefits, but it can cause problems.

A PROBLEM OF SCALE

Hydroelectric power does not cause pollution, and is a renewable source of energy. However, some hydroelectric projects are on a vast scale, with enormous dams that flood wide areas to create artificial lakes, which ruin farmland and make many people homeless.

The Hoover Dam in the USA was completed in the 1930s. Today many people are against building such huge dams.

SMALL IS BEAUTIFUL

Small-scale hydroelectric schemes use the moving water of local rivers and streams to generate enough electricity to supply a village – without the need to build a dam or flood important farmland.

Protesters campaign to halt the progress of a project to build large dams along the Narmada Valley in India. While the dams will provide hydroelectric power, they threaten the homes and livelihoods of millions of people.

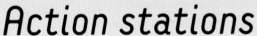

Action stations

The Intermediate Technology Development Group (ITDG), founded in 1966 by Dr E.F. Schumacher, sees the use of water as the key to improving the lives of many people who live in poverty in the developing world.

In one of its water-based projects, the ITDG helped to bring electricity to the 1,000 people living in the Kenyan village of Mbuiru — using a small-scale micro-hydro-power system that harnessed the energy of falling water from a nearby river. No dam was needed. The villagers constructed the tank that holds the water before it is directed downhill, through pipes, to a turbine.

Solutions for the future

There are many ideas and technologies – old and new – that can help improve the world's water supplies. But education is the key to success. We can all learn to play our part in making water safe, clean and available to all.

DESALINATION

New technology can turn salt water into fresh water by the process of desalination (de-salting). At the moment, the equipment is too expensive for many countries that could benefit from it. But as the technology becomes cheaper, its use will become more widespread.

There are about 12,500 desalination plants like this one in the world. Wealthy oil-producing countries, such as those in the Middle East, can afford the expensive technology involved.

TOWING WATER

One unusual way of bringing water, from where it is plentiful to where it is not, is to tow it. Some Greek islands deal with their water shortages by towing bags of fresh water from mainland Greece. Another technique involves polar icebergs, which are towed to warmer water, where fresh water is collected as it melts.

Icebergs of a suitable size and shape are selected using satellite photographs. Cables are attached to them so they can be towed to warmer water.

Action stations

For thousands of years in Africa and South America, people have harvested water from the fog or mist by gathering the moisture trapped on leaves. New technology has developed this old idea in a water scheme in Chile.

The water supply to the remote village of Chungungo has been increased by making use of the dense fog that often surrounds the village. Huge mesh nets trap the fog. The water droplets are collected and run to the village through a series of pipes.

The mist collection scheme in Chungungo provides each of the villagers with 40 litres of water a day. Before this, only 15 litres a day was available.

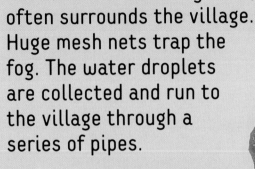

Glossary

Aquifer An underground store of water held in porous rocks (rocks containing many holes).

Condensation The process of turning from a gas to a liquid.

Desalination The process of removing salt from sea water to create fresh water.

Developed world The wealthier countries of the world, in which there are highly developed industries.

Developing world The poorer countries in the world, which rely more on farming than on industry.

Drought A long period without rain.

Ecovillage A community of people who aim to live in a way that does not damage the environment.

Evaporation The process of turning from water to water vapour. This happens when water is heated.

Fertilisers Substances added to soil to make plants grow faster or bigger. Fertilizers can be natural, but many farmers use chemical fertilizers that can cause water pollution.

Fossil fuels Fuels such as coal, oil and natural gas that are formed from the remains of plants and animals. Burning fossil fuels produces the greenhouse gas carbon dioxide.

Fresh water Water that contains less than 0.2% salt – as opposed to sea water, which is salty.

Geothermal This describes the heat from deep inside the Earth, which sometimes reaches the Earth's surface as hot springs or geysers.

Global warming The gradual rise in the Earth's temperature.

Greenhouse gases Gases such as carbon dioxide that are produced by burning fossil fuels. These gases trap heat in the atmosphere, so that it cannot escape into space.

Groundwater Water that lies beneath the ground, in soil and porous rocks.

Hydroelectric power Electricity generated by the movement of water.

Irrigation The watering of land for growing crops.

Latrine A basic toilet, not connected to a sewer system.

Micro-organism A very small organism (living thing) that can only be seen with a microscope.

Pollute To release harmful substances into the environment.

Sanitation The provision of such things as toilets and washing facilities to help keep people healthy, and prevent the spread of disease.

Sustainable Something that does not damage or remove natural resources, but leaves the environment in good order for the future.

Water cycle Water's never-ending cycle of evaporation and condensation from liquid to vapour and back to liquid.

Water table The top level of water stored in the ground.

Wetland An area of land that is soaked with water – such as swamps, bogs, marshes and creeks.

Find out more

www.wateraid.org.uk This website of the WaterAid charity features a 'learn zone' and information on current water and sanitation issues.

www.epa.gov Website of the US Environmental Protection Agency containing lots of information on water topics, from water supply to water treatment and conservation.

www.itdg.org The ITDG website provides practical answers to poverty and includes water-related news articles, for example about flooding and rainwater harvesting.

www.floridasprings.org Find out about how springs form, how to help protect them and see photographs from Florida Springs.

www.savewater.com.au Australian website featuring information about water conservation, including advice, products and news.

www.sas.org.uk Includes information about water problems, SAS campaigns and possible solutions to water pollution.

www.worldwatercouncil.org Website designed to promote awareness of water issues including conservation and supply.

Index